No. 4

Summary of National Vegetation Classification woodland descriptions

A. M. Whitbread*

K. J. Kirby**

Northminster House

Peterborough

PE1 1UA

* Current address: Sussex Wildlife Trust, Woods Mill, Henfield, Sussex

** Now with English Nature at above address

Further cop... ...ation Branch.
Joint Natu... ...use, City Road,

Copyri... ...Nature ...servation Committee 1992
ISB... ...01-04-7

Introduction

The first volume of British Plant Communities[1] was published in February 1991. It provides a detailed account of eighteen woodland and seven scrub communities, their composition, structure and distribution, their affinities to other types of vegetation, both in Britain and on the Continent, and the relation of the national vegetation classification types to those previously described for example using the Stand Type system[2].

The *summary descriptions* provided here are derived directly from the full accounts prepared by John Rodwell but are not a substitute for them. Rather they are intended as an *aide memoir* to assist surveyors in the field. Anyone who uses this should check their results periodically against the species tables and descriptions in British Plant Communities.

A series of *dendrograms* have been produced to show the broad relationships between the main communities (pages 4,5) and between the sub-communities for each community where these exist. These dendrograms are not keys and should not be followed slavishly. Particular care should be taken when deciding between types W8 & W9, between W10 & W11, and between W16 & W17. In south-west England, Wales and northern England and parts of southern Scotland both communities in each pair may occur. When in doubt explore the alternative pathways and refer to the descriptions.

We hope that you find it useful and would welcome any comments on how it might be improved. A brief account of how to use the classification in surveys is also being prepared.

Keith Kirby
Tony Whitbread
June 1991

1. Rodwell, J. 1991. *British plant communities*. Cambridge, Cambridge University Press.

2. Peterken, G.F. 1981. *Woodland conservation and management*. London, Chapman & Hall.

An overview of NVC woodland and scrub types (Types W19–25 are not included in this summary)

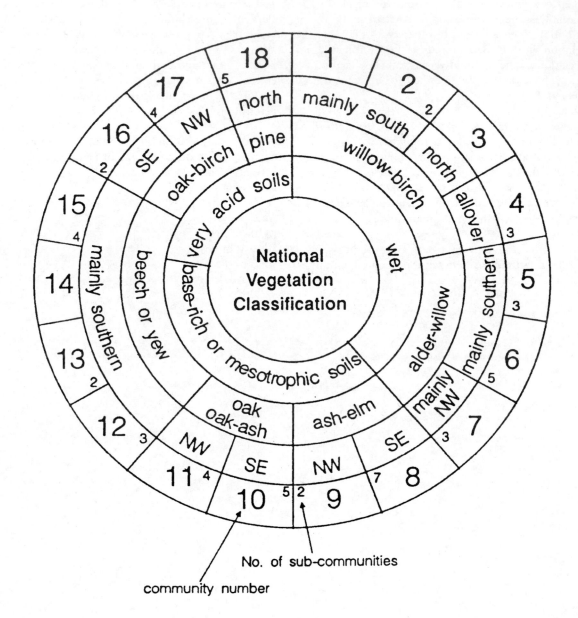

No. of sub-communities

community number

scrub		sub communities
W19	northern juniper scrub	2
W20	montane dwarf willow scrub	-
W21	hawthorn scrub	4
W22	blackthorn scrub	3
W23	gorse scrub	3
W24	bramble underscrub	2
W25	bracken-bramble underscrub	2

Contents

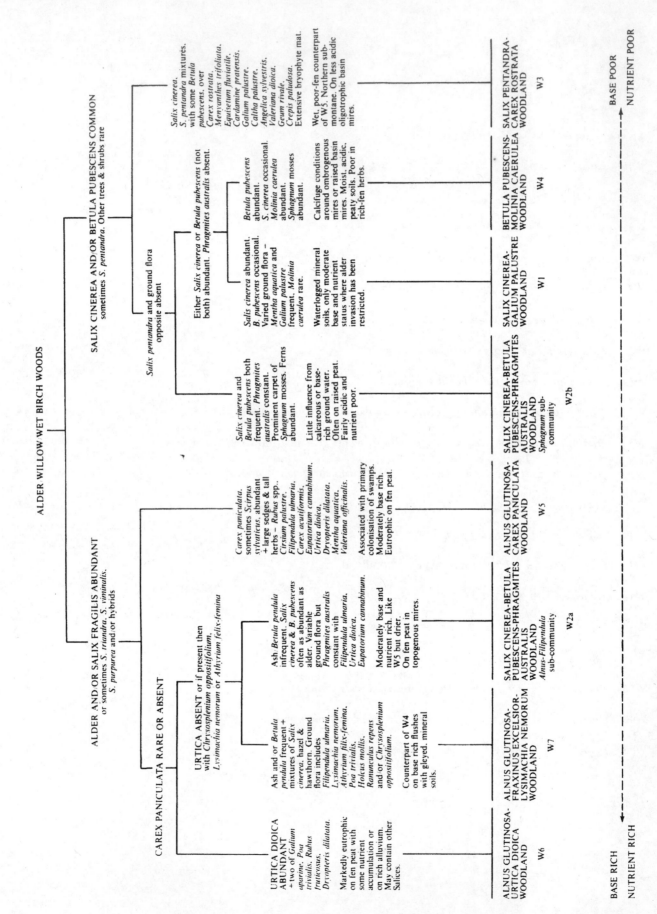

ALDER WILLOW/WET BIRCH WOODS

ALDER AND/OR SALIX FRAGILIS ABUNDANT or sometimes *S. triandra. S. viminalis. S. purpurea* and/or hybrids

SALIX CINEREA AND/OR BETULA PUBESCENS COMMON sometimes *S. pentandra.* Other trees & shrubs rare

---

CAREX PANICULATA RARE OR ABSENT

URTICA DIOICA ABUNDANT + two of *Galium aparine, Poa trivialis, Rubus fruticosus, Dryopteris dilatata.* Markedly eutrophic on fen peat with some nutrient accumulation or on rich alluvium. May contain other Salices.

URTICA ABSENT or if present then with *Chrysosplenium oppositifolium, Lysimachia nemorum* or *Athyrium felix-femina*

Ash and/or *Betula pendula* frequent + mixtures of *Salix cinerea,* hazel & hawthorn. Ground flora includes *Filipendula ulmaria, Lysimachia nemorum, Athyrium filix-femina, Poa trivialis, Holcus mollis, Ranunculus repens* and/or *Chrysosplenium oppositifolium.* Counterpart of W4 on base rich flushes with gleyed mineral soils.

Ash *Betula pendula* infrequent. *Salix cinerea* & *B. pubescens* often as abundant as alder. Variable ground flora but *Phragmites australis* constant with *Filipendula ulmaria. Urtica dioica. Eupatorium cannabinum.* Moderately base and nutrient rich. Like W5 but drier. On fen peat in topogenous mires.

Carex paniculata, sometimes *Scirpus sylvaticus,* abundant + large sedges & tall herbs – *Rubus* spp. *Cirsium palustre. Carex acutiformis. Filipendula ulmaria. Eupatorium cannabinum. Urtica dioica. Dryopteris dilatata. Mentha aquatica. Valeriana officinalis.* Associated with primary colonisation of swamps. Moderately base rich. Eutrophic on fen peat.

ALNUS GLUTINOSA- URTICA DIOICA WOODLAND W6

ALNUS GLUTINOSA- FRAXINUS EXCELSIOR- LYSIMACHIA NEMORUM WOODLAND W7

SALIX CINEREA-BETULA PUBESCENS-PHRAGMITES AUSTRALIS WOODLAND *Alnus-Filipendula* sub-community W2a

ALNUS GLUTINOSA- CAREX PANICULATA WOODLAND W5

Salix pentandra and ground flora opposite absent

Either *Salix cinerea* or *Betula pubescens* (not both) abundant. *Phragmites australis* absent.

Salix cinerea and *Betula pubescens* both frequent. *Phragmites australis* constant. Prominent carpet of *Sphagnum* mosses abundant. Ferns abundant. Little influence from calcareous or base-rich ground water. Often on raised peat. Fairly acidic and nutrient poor.

Salis cinerea abundant. *B. pubescens* occasional. Varied ground flora – *Mentha aquatica* and *Galium palustre* frequent, *Molinia caerulea* rare. Waterlogged mineral soils, only moderate base and nutrient status where alder invasion has been restricted.

Betula pubescens abundant. *S. cinerea* occasional. *Molinia caerulea* abundant. *Sphagnum* mosses abundant. Calcifuge conditions around ombrogenous mires or raised basin mires. Moist, acidic, peaty soils. Poor in rich-fen herbs.

Salix cinerea. S. pentandra mixtures. with some *Betula pubescens,* over *Carex rostrata, Menyanthes trifoliata, Equisetum fluviatile, Cardamine pratensis, Galium palustre, Caltha palustre, Angelica sylvestris, Valeriana dioica, Geum rivale, Crepis paludosa.* Extensive bryophyte mat. Wet, poor-fen counterpart of W5. Northern sub-montane. On less acidic oligotrophic basin mires.

SALIX CINEREA-BETULA PUBESCENS-PHRAGMITES AUSTRALIS WOODLAND *Sphagnum* sub-community W2b

SALIX CINEREA- GALIUM PALUSTRE WOODLAND W1

BETULA PUBESCENS- MOLINIA CAERULEA WOODLAND W4

SALIX PENTANDRA- CAREX ROSTRATA WOODLAND W3

BASE RICH
NUTRIENT RICH

BASE POOR
NUTRIENT POOR

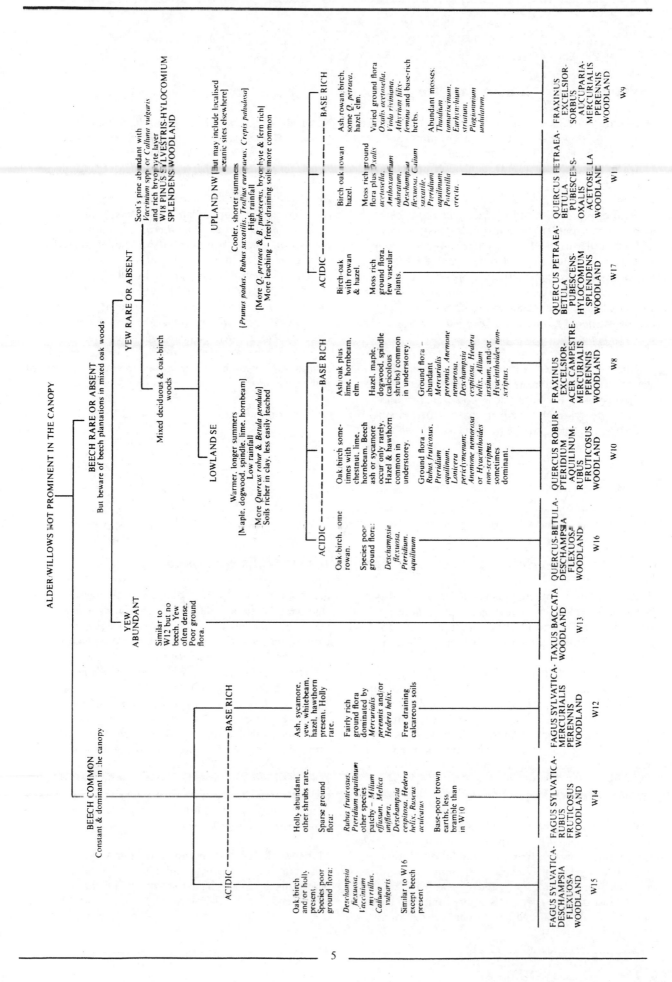

ALDER/WILLOWS NOT PROMINENT IN THE CANOPY

Salix cinerea – Galium palustre woodland

A community of wet mineral soils on the margins of standing or slow-moving water and in moist hollows, mainly in the lowlands. It often occurs as a narrow fringe or as scattered fragments around ponds, lakes, dune slacks etc.

The canopy is dominated by *Salix cinerea* but its structure is irregular. Young stands consist of a mass of bushes of variable height, older stands are more regular with a single tier of sallows *c.* 4-8m high. Other woody associates are only occasional – *Betula pubescens* with scarce *Alnus glutinosa, Quercus robur* & *Betula pendula*. Other Salices are uncommon but there can be scattered *Crataegus monogyna, Corylus avellana* and *Frangula alnus*.

The field layer varies in its cover and composition but the general appearance is of an open scatter of herbs. *Galium palustre* is common. *Mentha aquatica* and *Juncus effusus* are also frequent with scattered *Angelica sylvestris, Lycopus europaeus, Ranunculus flammula,* *R. repens, Epilobium palustre, Equisetum fluviatile, Filipendula ulmaria, Cirsium palustre, Rumex sanguineus, Caltha palustris, Hydrocotyle vulgaris, Potentilla palustris* and *Iris pseudacorus*. Scramblers such as *Rubus fruticosus, Solanum dulcamara* and *Hedera helix* may be abundant. In other cases the field layer has a grassy appearance – *Holcus lanatus, Agrostis canina* and *A. stolonifera*. Generally swamp and fen dominants are rare but occasional stands have some *Carex paniculata, C. riparia, C. vesicaria* or *Phragmites australis*. Bare ground or with a patchy cover of bryophytes can be quite extensive. *Eurhynchium praelongum* is most frequent with some *Chiloscyphus polyanthos, Calliergon cuspidatum, C. cordifolium, Brachythecium rutabulum* and *Rhytidiadelphus squarrosus*. Epiphytic lichens may be conspicuous in sheltered situations to the south-west of Britain.

No sub-communities

Salix cinerea – Betula pubescens – Phragmites australis woodland

A community of topogenous fen-peats on flood plain mires, terraces of river valley mires and, more rarely, on basin mires where litter accumulation has raised the peat surface above the level of winter flooding.

Salix cinerea and *Betula pubescens* are the most frequent species with some *Alnus*. Abundance of any one of these is determined as much by colonisation probabilities as it is by differing habitat requirements of the species so that there is not a set sequence of colonisation of the previous fen communities. Other woody species can be locally dominant, particularly in early stages of colonisation – eg *Frangula alnus, Rhamnus catharticus*.

The composition and structure of the field layer is strongly influenced by the preceeding fen. Since these fen communities can be very variable, the field layer of W2 has few constant species. *Phragmites australis* is most frequent overall but its cover may vary – it can form dense stands. occur as scattered individuals but is only rarely absent altogether. Other fen dominants occur sporadically, often confined to younger, open canopies. These include *Carex acutiformis, Cladium mariscus, Calamagrostis canescens* and *C. epigejos*. *Carex paniculata* can occur but is more typical of W5. Tall herbs and ferns are very patchy – *Thelypteris palustris* is quite frequent with scattered *Filipendula ulmaria, Eupatorium cannabinum, Lysimachia vulgaris, Lythrum salicaria* and rare *Peucedanum palustre*. These are more frequently found in the rich fen *Alnus-Filipendula* sub-community. *Rubus fruticosus* or *Rosa canina* tangles are often present with, less commonly, some *Rubus idaeus, Ribes nigrum* and *R. rubrum*. *Dryopteris dilatata*, usually uncommon in fens, may be present here. There can be very extensive areas of bare ground interspersed with loose mats of *Poa trivialis* and *Eurhynchium praelongum*.

Floristic differences between sub-communities reflect variation in base-richness and calcium levels in the peat. This is largely dependent on the height and movement of ground water.

2a ———————————————|——————————————— 2b

ALNUS GLUTINOSA-FILIPENDULA ULMARIA SUB-COMMUNITY

Characteristic of fen peats which are influenced by the fluctuating water table. The pH is high – 6.5 to 7.5. Fairly eutrophic conditions.

More species rich and structurally complex than b. Alder is preferential with occasional ash and scarce oak. *Phragmites australis* and/or *Carex acutiformis* often dominate the field layer with frequent *Filipendula ulmaria*, *Eupatorium cannabinum* and *Urtica dioica*. Occasional species include *Cirsium palustre*, *Angelica sylvestris*, *Phalaris arundinacea*, *Berula erecta*, *Lycopus europaeus*, *Lythrum salicaria* and *Lysimachia vulgaris*. A *Rubus fruticosus* underscrub often occurs with climbers like *Galium palustre*, *G. aparine*, *Solanum dulcamara*, *Calystegia sepium*, *Tamus communis*, *Humulus lupulus* and *Lonicera periclymenum*. Ferns are not as abundant as in b. Small herbs are not numerous apart from mats of *Poa trivialis*, scattered *Mentha aquatica* and *Caltha palustris*. Expanses of bare earth and peat may have extensive bryophyte carpets but the species involved are few – *Eurhynchium praelongum*, *Brachythecium rutabulum* and *Plagiomnium undulatum*. Unlike sub-community b, *Sphagna* are characteristically scarce.

There are several variants of this sub-community in, for example, Wicken Fen and Woodwalton Fen.

SPHAGNUM SUB-COMMUNITY

Found where peat levels are high enough to be isolated from the effects of ground water – either where peat has accumulated to raise levels or on floating peat rafts (so the peat level is always above the water level).

Betula pubescens is the most abundant woody species with a little *Salix cinerea* but alder and ash are less common than in a. *Frangula alnus* and *Salix aurita* are local but oak, *Rhamnus catharticus* and *Viburnum opulus* are characteristically absent. *Myrica gale* and *Salix repens* can form a patchy lower tier with some *Rubus fruticosus*, *Rosa canina* and *Lonicera periclymenum*. *Phragmites australis* remains frequent but other fen monocots are sparse and *Carex acutiformis* absent. Tall fen herbs are also patchy in comparison to a. Grasses are often more abundant – *Holcus lanatus*, *Molinia caerulea*, *Agrostis canina*, *Agrostis stolonifera* and *Poa trivialis*. Abundance of ferns is characteristic – *Thelypteris palustris*, *Dryopteris dilatata*, *D. carthusiana*, *D. cristata*, *Athyrium filix-femina* and more rarely *Thelypteris phegopteris* and *Osmunda regalis*. The *Sphagna* are also characteristically abundant here, sometimes forming a virtually continuous cover – *S. fimbriatum*, *S. squarrosum*, *S. palustre*, *S. recurvum* and *S. subnitens*.

Salix pentandra – Carex rostrata woodland

A community of peat soils kept moist by moderately base-rich and calcareous ground water in open water transitions, most common in northern Britain. Its general geographic limits are heavily influenced by climate, many of the species characterising W3 tending to have a northerly distribution.

This type is fairly constant in its composition and structure. The canopy is low, uneven-topped and dominated by *Salix* spp, usually *S. pentandra* and/or *S. cinerea*. Other Salices are rare but can be locally abundant – *S. nigricans*, *S. phylicifolia* and *S. aurita*, more rarely *S. viminalis* and *S. purpurea*. *Betula pubescens* occurs occasionally but *Alnus glutinosa* is rare. Southern fen species like *Frangula alnus*, *Rhamnus catharticus* and *Viburnum opulus* are generally absent.

The field layer can vary widely. Many stands have several species co-dominating, but the overall assemblage of species is distinctive. Tall herbs and horsetails are the most prominent feature, for example *Filipendula ulmaria*, *Angelica sylvestris*, *Valeriana dioica*, *V. officinalis*, *Geum rivale*, *Cirsium palustre* and *Equisetum fluviatile*, but rich fen species (eg *Eupatorium cannabinum*, *Lysimachia vulgaris*, *Lythrum salicaria*, *Iris pseudacorus*) are usually absent. Shorter herbs often form a patchy lower layer, for example *Cardamine pratensis* and *Crepis paludosa* and lesser amounts of *Caltha palustris*, *Mentha aquatica*, *Lychnis flos-cuculi*, *Ranunculus repens*, *Poa trivialis*, *Dactylorhiza fuchsii*, *Equisetum palustre*, *Menyanthes trifoliata*, *Potentilla palustre* and *Galium palustre*. Ferns are not a prominent feature. Large grasses, rushes and sedges may or may not be abundant. *Carex rostrata* occurs most frequently but usually as sparse scattered shoots. Less frequent are *C. diandra*, *C. lasiocarpa*, *C. appropinquata*, *C. paniculata*, *C. laevigata*, *C. vesicaria*, *C. nigra*, *C. curta*, *Juncus acutiflorus* and *J. effusus*. Bryophytes are abundant, sometimes forming a complete ground carpet. *Calliergon cuspidatum*, *Climacium dendroides* and *Rhizomnium punctatum* tend to be the most conspicuous with some *Plagiomnium affine*, *P. ellipticum*, *P. rostratum*, *P. elatum*, *Mnium hornum* and *Eurhynchium praelongum*. Patches of *Sphagnum* spp. may be locally abundant.

No sub-communities

Betula pubescens – Molinia caerulea

A community of moist, moderately acidic, though not necessarily highly oligotrophic, peaty soils. It is characteristic of thin or drying ombrogenous peats which are isolated from the influence of base-rich or eutrophic ground waters but is also found on peaty gleys flushed by rather base- and nutrient-poor water.

Betula pubescens is the most common woody species and is usually dominant, forming a rather open canopy of well-spaced individuals. Other trees are uncommon. *B. pendula* is generally scarce but can be frequent in drier stands. *Alnus glutinosa* is rarely abundant but tends to be more frequent in the *Juncus* sub-community. *Quercus* spp. and *Fraxinus excelsior* are very scarce. The understorey is generally sparse.

Salix cinerea is the most frequent shrub layer species although locally *S. caprea*, *S. pentandra*, *S. aurita*, *Corylus avellana*, *Crataegus monogyna* and *Ilex aquifolium* may occur.

The great abundance of *Molinia caerulea* is the most distinctive feature of the field layer and other species may be limited to areas between tussocks. *Sphagnum* spp. are usually present, most typically *S. palustre*, and *S. recurvum* with some *S. subnitens*, sometimes forming a continuous carpet. Other mosses such as *Aulocomnium palustre*, *Eurhynchium praelongum* and *Pseudoscleropodium purum* are sometimes common while eroding *Molinia* tussocks may be covered by *Polytrichum commune*.

Sphagnum spp. rare. Field layer with frequent *Rubus fruticosus*. *Dryopteris dilatata* and *Lonicera periclymenum*.

4a

DRYOPTERIS DILATATA – RUBUS FRUTICOSUS SUB-COMMUNITY

Longer established, drier stands on thin peat. Some local nutrient enrichment or disturbance often marked by presence of *Epilobium angustifolium*.

Woody component more variable than in b and c. Some *Betula pendula*. *Sorbus aucuparia* and oak. *Salix cinerea* understorey sometimes present.
[Nb These field layer species can also be
[abundant under *Betula pubescens* rich
[canopies of the *B. pubescens* sub-
[community of Alnus-Urtica (W6e) woodland
[but the frequency of *U. dioica* and absence
[of *Molinia* there should effect a separation.

Prominent carpet of mixtures of *Sphagnum fimbriatum*, *S. recurvum*, *S. palustre*, *S. squarrosum* and *S. papillosum* with *Molinia caerulea* the only prominent grass.

4c

SPHAGNUM SUB-COMMUNITY

Wetter sites on deeper peat.

Betula pubescens dominant, few other trees and shrubs. Flora typical of wet heath or mire – *Calluna vulgaris*, *Erica tetralix*, *Eriophorum vaginatum*, *E. angustifolium*, *Carex nigra*, *Vaccinium oxycoccus*, *Carex rostrata*, *Menyanthes trifoliata* and *Potentilla palustris*. *Sphagna* found in wet runnels between *Molinia caerulea* tussocks.

Sphagnum recurvum and less often *S. palustre* may be prominent but the field layer also has frequent *Holcus mollis*, *H. lanatus*, *Deschampsia cespitosa* and *Juncus effusus*.

4b

JUNCUS EFFUSUS SUB-COMMUNITY

Acidic soligenous mire conditions and emerging base-poor flushes.

Alder more frequent than in a and c. Some *Salix cinerea* but no understorey. Grassy field layer, tussocks of sedges and rushes between *Molinia caerulea*. Some *Juncus articulatus*, *Carex laevigata*, *C. nigra*, *Potentilla erecta*, *Hydrocotyle vulgaris*, *Viola palustris*, *Cirsium palustre* and *Lotus uliginosus* but *Carex remota* absent.

Alnus glutinosa – Carex paniculata woodland

A community of wet to waterlogged organic soils on topogenous or soligenous mires which are base rich and moderately eutrophic. It is associated with fen peats in open water transitions, flood plain mires and basin mires where there is strong influence from base-rich ground waters.

The floristic richness of the community is related to the richness of preceding swamp and fen communities. *Alnus glutinosa* and *Salix cinerea* are the most frequent invaders of these communities so that young stands often have a co-dominance of these in low, uneven, open canopies. As the stand ages *Alnus* tends to exclude *S. cinerea* or relegates it to the understorey. Well-established stands may thus have a clearly defined canopy of multi-stemmed *Alnus*, with scattered associated trees over a distinct understorey of varying density. This pattern can be complicated by trees falling or blowing over. As the water level rises *Alnus* may die so that dead emergent trees are a common feature in this community. *Betula pubescens* may be present in patches with *Fraxinus excelsior* and *Quercus robur* in drier stands. *Crataegus monogyna, Ilex aquifolium, Sorbus aucuparia, Rhamnus catharticus, Viburnum opulus* and *Frangula alnus* occur occasionally and the latter can be dense in young stands.

The field layer reflects the flora of the preceding fen or swamp with a small woodland component. The large sedges are conspicuous – *Carex paniculata* and *C. acutiformis* with some *C. elata, C. appropinquata, C. riparia* and *C. pseudocyperus*. Other fen elements also prominent include *Phragmites australis, Urtica dioica, Filipendula ulmaria, Eupatorium cannabinum, Cirsium palustre, Valeriana officianalis, V. dioica, Iris pseudacorus, Angelica sylvestris, Lysimachia vulgaris, Lythrum salicaria* and *Peucedanum palustre*. Among these taller species woodland plants like *Geranium robertianum* and *Circaea lutetiana* may be found; less often *Mentha aquatica, Poa trivialis, Ranunculus repens, R. flammula, Viola palustris, Hydrocotyle vulgaris* and *Caltha palustris*. Sprawling and scrambling species such as *Galium palustre, Solanum dulcamara, Rubus* spp., *Lonicera periclymenum, Ribes nigrum, R. rubrum* and *Rosa* spp. may be abundant. Ferns are often conspicuous – *Dryopteris dilatata* and the occasional *Athyrium filix-femina, Dryopteris carthusiana, D. cristata, Thelypteris palustris* and *Osmunda regalis*. Mosses such as *Eurhynchium praelongum, Brachythecium rutabulum, Plagiomnium undulatum* and *Rhizomnium punctatum* are common around sedge tussocks. *Sphagna* are rare but may occur along base poor seepage where *Pellia epiphylla* is particularly characteristic.

Ash. *Betula pubescens* and *Salix cinerea* frequent canopy associates. sometimes locally dominant. *Chrysosplenium oppositifolium* and *Pellia epiphylla* rare.

5a

Frangula alnus rare. rich-fen dicots and ferns rare. Field layer dominated by *Carex paniculata* and/or *C. acutiformis* (locally *Scirpus sylvaticus*) with *Phragmites australis* and *Filipendula ulmaria*.

5b

Frangula alnus frequent. Field layer a rich mixture of sedges. *Carex paniculata, C. acutiformis* and *C. remota*, rich fen dicots – *Lysimachia vulgaris, Lythrum salicaria, Lycopus europaeus* and *Peucedanum palustre*, and ferns – *Thelypteris palustris* and *Osmunda regalis*.

5c

Pure alder canopy. *Chrysosplenium oppositifolium* and *Pellia epiphylla* often prominent as a ground cover carpet.

PHRAGMITES AUSTRALIS SUB-COMMUNITY

Alder dominant, some ash and *Betula pendula*, over *Salix cinerea*. Field layer poorer than b and c. Tall herbs and sedges prominent. *Equisetum palustre* is a weak preferential. *Solanum dulcamara* is more frequent here than in b and c, sometimes forming a dense underscrub.

LYSIMACHIA VULGARIS SUB-COMMUNITY

Canopy as a. but shrubs more varied - *Frangula alnus* and *Viburnum opulus* preferential. *Carex remota, C. elongata* preferential. *Impatiens capensis. Thalictrum flavum, Myosotis laxa, Cardamine pratensis, Scutellaria galericulata, Viola palustris, Ranunculus repens* and *R. flammula* more common than in a and c. Ferns may be abundant.

The most species rich of the sub-communities.

CHRYSOSPLENIUM OPPOSITIFOLIUM SUB-COMMUNITY

Typical of springs and seepage lines associated with the emergence of less base-rich water. Soils have a mineral base with some peat accumulation. Calcicoles not as frequent. Tree and shrub layer simpler and less diverse than in a and b. Hawthorn absent. *Carex paniculata* dominant. less *C. acutiformis*. Other sedges and *Phragmites australis* rare. Tall herbs less rich but *Oenanthe crocata* preferential. Small herbs and bryophytes form a distinct patchy carpet between sedge tussocks.

Alnus glutinosa – Urtica dioica woodland

A community of eutrophic moist soils, typically either sites where there has been substantial deposition of mineral matter or on flood plain mires where enriched waters flood fen peat. The community is rather ill-defined. There are a variety of canopy dominants – *Alnus glutinosa*, *Salix* spp. and *Betula pubescens* – and the field layer is generally species-poor.

Overall *Alnus glutinosa* is the commonest tree particularly on the wetter soils. However, it is replaced by *Salix fragilis* in one sub-community and by *Betula pubescens* on drier sites. Other trees are uncommon. *Populus nigra* is rare but distinctive where it occurs whilst *Acer pseudoplatanus*, *Fraxinus excelsior* and *Quercus robur* occur occasionally. There is usually an open patchy understorey. *Salix cinerea* is the most common shrub with *Crataegus monogyna* and *Sambucus nigra* on drier ground. *Salix caprea*, *Ilex aquifolium*, *Corylus avellana*, *Viburnum opulus* and *Prunus spinosa* are generally sparse. The osiers *Salix viminalis*, *S. triandra* and *S. purpurea* may be abundant in some stands.

The feature distinguishing this community from closely related types is the poor representation of large swamp and tall fen species. *Urtica dioica* is the really typical herb layer species and sometimes forms a virtual monoculture. There are few other common field layer species but those that are present show an ill-defined transition from the wetter to the drier habitats. Where soils are moist towards the surface *Poa trivialis* and *Galium aparine* are frequent with some *Solanum dulcamara*. There may also be clumps of swamp and fen species. On drier substrates these species are less important whilst *Lonicera periclymenum*, *Dryopteris dilatata* and *Rubus fruticosus* increase in prominence. Other less frequent species include *Arrhenatherum elatius*, *Heracleum sphondylium*, *Ranunculus repens*, *Cardamine flexuosa*, *Glechoma hederacea*, *Angelica sylvestris* and *Cirsium palustre*. This field layer is often associated with a "run-down" appearance, stands often being choked with brush-wood from winter flooding whilst drier stands show signs of disturbance.

W6

Rubus fruticosus often abundant, frequently with *Dryopteris dilatata* and *Lonicera periclymenum*. On drier substrates.

Salix fragilis dominant or co-dominant with alder. Elder frequent. Sprawling *Solanum dulcamara* in the shrub layer.

6b

Salix fragilis and osiers rare. Alder dominated canopy over *S. cinerea* shrub layer.

6a

Elder and *Salix cinerea* frequent in the shrub layer. *Dryopteris felix-mas* and *Hedera helix* frequent in the field layer.

6d

Betula pubescens often more frequent than alder. Self seeding or planted pine sometimes present. Elder, *S. cinerea*, *Dryopteris felix-mas* and *Hedera helix* infrequent.

6e

Managed or derelict osier beds dominated by *Salix triandra, S. viminalis* and *S. purpurea.*

6c

SALIX VIMINALIS; S. TRIANDRA SUB-COMMUNITY

On freshly colonised alluvium. Osiers dominate over a typical W6 field layer. Occasional emergent alder and ash.

SALIX FRAGILIS SUB-COMMUNITY

Understorey often choked with decaying fallen *Salix fragilis* branches. *Urtica dioica* luxuriant with dense *Galium aparine*. Often extensive stretches of sloppy mud.

TYPICAL SUB-COMMUNITY

Occasional ash, sycamore and oak. Thin shrub layer. Abundant *Urtica dioica* with much *Galium aparine, Poa trivialis, Ranunculus repens, Glechoma hederacea, Arrhenatherum elatius, Heracleum sphondylium, Solanum dulcamara* and *Humulus lupulus.*

SAMBUCUS NIGRA SUB-COMMUNITY

As dry as, but more eutrophic and base rich than, e. Alder dominant, *Betula pubescens* occasional. *Urtica dioica* and *Galium aparine* not as prominent as in a and b. *Circaea luteiana, Geum urbanum* and *Mercurialis perennis* are present where there is local base enrichment. *Allium ursinum* and *Petasites hybridus* can be locally dominant.

BETULA PUBESCENS SUB-COMMUNITY

Shrub layer very sparse. *Salix cinerea* absent. *Urtica dioica, Galium aparine* and *Poa trivialis* less abundant than elsewhere. *Rubus fruticosus/Lonicera periclymenum/Dryopteris dilatata* underscrub is the most obvious feature. *Epilobium angustifolium* and *Holcus lanatus* preferential.

WETTER SITUATIONS

DRIER SITUATIONS

Alnus glutinosa – Fraxinus excelsior – Lysimachia nemorum woodland

A woodland type typical of moist to very wet mineral soils which are only moderately base-rich and not very eutrophic. It is most extensive in the wetter parts of Britain, but usually on soils where there is no great tendency for peat accumulation.

Stands often have a somewhat open, irregular canopy. *Alnus glutinosa* is the main woody species and can be overwhelmingly dominant. However *Fraxinus excelsior*, *Salix cinerea*, *S. caprea* and, less commonly, *Betula pubescens* can also be locally abundant. *Acer pseudoplatanus* may occur where the soils are not permanently moist. *Quercus robur* is sparse, this being a predominantly north-western type and *Q. petraea* can occur in the less strongly gleyed soils of the *Deschampsia* sub-community. *Corylus avellana* and *Crataegus monogyna* are found in the understorey in the drier areas with *Salix cinerea* on damper sites. *Sorbus aucuparia*, *Sambucus nigra*, *Ilex aquifolium*, *Viburnum opulus*, *Prunus spinosa* and *Prunus padus* may also be present.

The field layer is usually a low growing cover of herbaceous dicotyledons and grasses – *Lysimachia nemorum*, *Ranunculus repens*, *Poa trivialis* and *Holcus mollis* are most common. *Filipendula ulmaria* and *Athyrium filix-femina* are more scattered but give a layered structure to the herbaceous vegetation. *Juncus effusus* is very frequent in some sub-communities. *Carex remota*, *C. pendula* and *C. laevigata* can occur in some quantity but *C. paniculata* and *C. acutiformis* are rare giving a good separation between this and other *Alnus-Carex* types. The local influence of more base-rich waters allows sporadic appearance of *Mercurialis perennis*, *Geum urbanum* and *Circaea lutetiana*. *Rubus fruticosus* frequently forms an underscrub. The bryophyte layer is patchy but *Eurhynchium praelongum* and *Plagiomnium undulatum* are frequent with some *Thuidium tamariscinum*, *Rhizomnium punctatum* and *Brachythecium rutabulum* and with *B. rivulare* and *Chiloscyphus polyanthos* in wetter areas.

Differences between sub-communities are related to the extent of waterlogging, the nature of the water supply and its movement.

W7

Ranunculus repens and *Chrysosplenium oppositifolium* constant as a ground carpet. *Urtica dioica, Galium aparine* and/or, less commonly *Phalaris arundinacea* dominant in the field layer. — **7a**

Chrysosplenium oppositifolium absent or, if present, then no with *Urtica dioica, Galium aparine* or *Phalaris arundinacea*.

Cirsium palustre and *Valeriana officinalis* frequent but dominants variable – *Carex remota, C. pendula, Equisetum telmateia, Carex laevigata* or *Juncus effusus*. Abundant bryophytes – *Brachythecium rivulare, Calliergon cuspidatum. C. polyanthos* and *Cratoneuron commutatum* preferential. — **7b**

Hazel and hawthorn the most frequent shrubs. Abundant *Deschampsia cespitosa, Dryopteris dilatata, Oxalis acetosella. Mnium hornum* and *Atrichum undulatum*. — **7c**

URTICA DIOICA SUB-COMMUNITY

On light textured alluvial soils on flat or gently sloping terraces of young river systems. Soils free-draining but kept moist by high water tables or by flushing from above.

Alder dominant but usually with some ash. but less birch. Sycamore may be present. Patchy understorey. hazel and hawthorn uncommon.

CAREX REMOTA – CIRSIUM PALUSTRE

Associated with springs or seepage lines where ground water emerges at impervious strata on shedding slopes. Can be massive slumping of soils producing an open, unstable vegetation cover.

Alder dominant but usually with ash and birch. *Salix cinerea* most common in the understorey. Sycamore typically absent. Field layer diverse and luxuriant, mostly tall herbs. sedges and *Equisetum* spp. Bryophytes important especially on patches of slipping. moist soil.

DESCHAMPSIA CESPITOSA SUB-COMMUNITY

On brown earths that show some signs of gleying and on base-rich soils with impeded drainage. Often occurs as a transition between flushes. *Alnus* shares dominance with *Fraxinus* and *B. pubescens*, sometimes with *Q. robur*. sycamore. wych elm or rowan. Well defined shrub layer. *S. cinerea* rare.

Fraxinus excelsior – Acer campestre – Mercurialis perennis woodland

A community of calcareous mull soils found mainly but not exclusively in the relatively warm, dry, lowlands of southern Britain. It is marked by the presence of species with a southern distribution which helps to separate the community from *Fraxinus-Sorbus-Mercurialis* types (W9). It occurs on soils derived from a variety of calcareous parent materials in the drier parts of the country where the affects of leaching are limited. Mull humus and the quick incorporation of plant material into the soil are characteristic of this community.

Soil variations are the main cause of differences between and within the two main suites of sub-communities. In the south-east W8 is rare on free-draining calcareous soils where *Fagus sylvatica* woodland (especially W12) tends to predominate. Instead W8 occurs on softer argillaceous rocks with a fairly impermeable clay soil and is associated with moderate terrain of gentle slopes and undulating plateaus. Differences between sub-communities in the south-east are related to the extent and duration of soil waterlogging. In the north-west of its range (upland-lowland borders) W8 occurs on limestones. The soils are free-draining yet moist and generally calcareous and base-rich. Thus clay soil species characteristic of the south eastern sub-communities are sparse whilst plants indicative of free-draining soils are more common. The topography is more sharply defined here with much steeper slopes.

Major variations within the tree and shrub layer
The presence of *Fraxinus excelsior*, *Acer campestre* and *Corylus avellana* are the main diagnostic features of this community but these are sometimes relegated to a minor role due to the local abundance of species which are only occasional throughout the community as a whole.

i.   One group of sub-communities (types a-c) have a south-eastern distribution. *Quercus robur* is the next most common species after the three above and is strongly preferential to this group. In addition there are other species which may achieve local dominance including *Tilia cordata*, *Carpinus betulus* and the invasive elms *Ulmus procera* and *U. carpinifolia*. *Tilia* and *Carpinus* may both occur as dense single species stands imposing a structural uniformity which has been further accentuated by generations of coppicing. However these species are not confined to this community and often form dense stands in *Quercus-Pteridium-Rubus*

woodland (W10). *Castanea sativa*, which is also locally abundant in W10, is rare in W8. Sub-communities a-c are more likely to occur in woods managed previously under a coppice-with-standards system. The canopy/understorey structure of high forests is often absent, although this is changing with the abandonment of coppicing. Hazel is the most frequent shrub, except in dense *Tilia* or *Carpinus* coppices. The hawthorns are also common and *Crataegus laevigata* is preferential to this group, particularly in long-established stands.

ii.   The second group of sub-communities (types e-g) are more common to the north and west. *Quercus petraea* and hybrids are more abundant here (but are not exclusive to these sub-communities) and *Ulmus glabra* and *Acer pseudoplatanus* are also more common. A high forest canopy/understorey structure is more common than in sub-communities a-c.

iii. Sub-community d is largely southern in its distribution, but overlaps the ranges of both the above groups and this is reflected in its tree and shrub layer.

On the lighter, base-rich soils of southern England *Fagus sylvatica* and *Taxus baccata* are common and form transitions between the types in i. (above) and types W12 and W13. To the north, away from its presumed natural range, *Fagus sylvatica* tends to dominate on lighter, acidic soils so does not pose the same problems of definition as in the south. There are also transitions between W8 and *Alnus* types (W5-W7) around flushes and on wet plateaus. *Alnus glutinosa* is generally rare in W8 but can become common on permanently waterlogged soils where the woodland merges with *Alnus-Fraxinus-Lysimachia* community (W7).

Common shrub species include *Crataegus monogyna*, *Sambucus nigra* (in more eutropic situations), *Prunus spinosa* (particularly as post-coppice and ride vegetation in the *Deschampsia* sub-community), *Cornus sanguineus*, *Euonymus europaeus* and *Ligustrum vulgare* (on the more base-rich soils), *Salix caprea* and *S. cinerea*.

Ground Flora
Mercurialis perennis is the most distinctive field layer species (but is also common in W9) with mixtures of *Hyacinthoides non-scriptus*, *Circaea lutetiana*, *Geum urbanum*, *Arum maculatum* and *Viola riviniana/*

reichenbachiana. Less frequent but still characteristic are *Lamiastrum galeobdolon, Carex sylvatica, Sanicula europaea, Adoxa moschatellina* and *Conopodium majus. Hedera helix* and *Brachypodium sylvaticum* are common in some sub-communities. These combinations can be found in other communities but usually with a different canopy or with other species such as ferns that are typically scarce in W8. *Rubus fruticosus* may be common with occasional *Rosa canina, Rubus idaeus, R. caesius, Ribes rubrum, R. uva-crispa* and *Lonicera periclymenum.* These may suppress the abundance of *Mercurialis perennis* such that the community can resemble W10. However, the presence of scattered *Circaea lutetiana, Geum urbanum* and *Arum maculatum* will usually aid separation. *Pteridium aquilinum* is usually rare in W8.

One group of herbs follows *Quercus robur, Carpinus betulus, Tilia cordata,* the invasive elms and *Crataegus laevigata* in being associated with heavier base-rich soils of the south-east (i. above). These are *Poa trivialis, Glechoma hederacea, Ajuga reptans, Primula vulgaris* (*P. elatior* in E Anglia), *Hyacinthoides non-scriptus* and *Rosa canina.* These species are less common in the north-west (ii. above) except on the moister soils. There the increase in *Acer pseudoplatanus, Ulmus glabra, Quercus petraea* and *Ilex aquifolium* is matched by greater abundance of *Urtica dioica, Galium aparine, Geranium robertianum* and *Phyllitis scolopendrium.*

Variation in the duration and extent of soil waterlogging results in variation in the abundance of *Mercurialis.* The *Primula-Glechoma* sub-community (a) is the central type. Where soils remain wetter longer the *Anemone* sub-community (b) takes over. The *Deschampsia* sub-community (c) is found mainly on soils which are free from waterlogging for only a short period in the summer. A further sub-community of the south is characterised by an abundance of *Hedera helix* (d). This is distinctive of the more oceanic south-west and also of younger woods on base-rich soils in the south-east.

In the north-west waterlogging plays a lesser role in the distinctions between the sub-communities. Species indicative of clay soils (eg *Hyacinthoides non-scriptus*) give way to species like *Brachypodium sylvaticum* and *Geranium robertianum* which readily colonise free-draining soils. *Sambucus nigra, Urtica dioica* and *Galium aparine* are more common in the *Geranium* sub-community (e), indicating a eutrophic type with high nutrient turnover. The *Allium ursinum* sub-community (f) is found on similar but moister slope-foot soils. The final north-west sub-community has a field layer which tends to reflect a patchy woody cover, a complex rocky topography and moderately montane climatic conditions. This is the *Teucrium scorodonia* sub-community (g).

W8

I — A south-eastern type. *Quercus robur* abundant, sycamore and wych elm rare. Heavy base-rich soils. Lime, hornbeam and *Crataegus laevigata* preferential. Ground flora indicative of mull soils – *Poa trivialis*, *Glechoma hederacea*, *Ajuga reptans*, *Primula* spp., *Hyacinthoides non-scriptus*.

Deschampsia cespitosa rare, frequent *Primula* spp. *Glechoma hederacea* and *Poa trivialis*

Deschampsia cespitosa constant-dominant *Primula* spp. and *Glechoma hederacea* rare.

Anemone nemorosa and *Ranunculus ficaria* rare.

Anemone nemorosa and *Ranunculus ficaria* constant vernal dominants.

8a   **8b**   **8c**

III — Continuous ground carpet of *Hedera*.

8d

PRIMULA VULGARIS-GLECHOMA HEDERACEA SUB-COMMUNITY

Central type. Ash, hazel and field maple generally frequent, often the basis of a coppice system. Lime and hornbeam locally dominant. Ground flora dominated by *Mercurialis perennis*. frequent *Poa trivialis*, *Glechoma hederacea*, *Ajuga reptans*, *Primula* spp. *Hyacinthoides non-scriptus* more prominent as soils become damper.

ANEMONE NEMOROSA SUB-COMMUNITY

Increasing waterlogging

Widespread type on heavy clay soils of the south-east and on local wet sites in the north-west. Characterised by spring-wet soils. Woody component as in the central type but hornbeam and *Populus tremula* more abundant. *Hyacinthoides non-scriptus* often more abundant than *Mercurialis perennis* but *Anemone nemorosa* and *Ranunculus ficaria* notably frequent. Few other preferentials – *Rumex sanguineus*. *Carex pendula*, *C. remota*, *C. strigosa* and *C. acutiformis*.

DESCHAMPSIA CESPITOSA SUB-COMMUNITY

Heavy, wet, often trampled soils. Abundance of *Mercurialis perennis* lower, also *Hyacinthoides non-scriptus* reduced. *Deschampsia cespitosa* the most obvious feature especially in open conditions - young coppice and rides. A habitat of damp disturbed conditions where diversity is increased by ruderal species, especially *Juncus effusus*, *J. conglomeratus*, *Rumex* spp.. *Cirsium* spp.. *Epilobium* spp. and *Hypericum* spp.

HEDERA HELIX SUB-COMMUNITY

Usually indicative of secondary woodland. Structure often simple, canopy and understorey dense. Ash or oak over hawthorn, hazel and sparse field maple. Species-poor ground flora. Mostly *Hedera helix* with some *Geum urbanum*, *Circaea lutetiana*, *Brachypodium sylvaticum* and *Poa trivialis*.

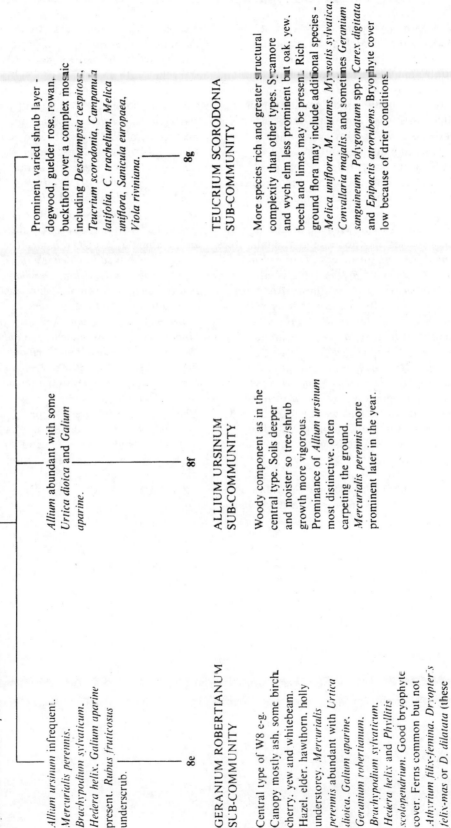

More north-westerly in distribution. Sycamore. wych elm and *Q. petraea* abundant, *Quercus robur* rarer. Light. well-drained but moist soils. Ground flora indicative of free draining soils. eg *Brachypodium sylvaticum* and *Geranium robertianum*. *Hyacinthoides non-scriptus* less common.

8e

Allium ursinum infrequent. *Mercurialis perennis*. *Brachypodium sylvaticum*. *Hedera helix*. *Galium aparine* present. *Rubus fruticosus* underscrub.

8f

Allium abundant with some *Urtica dioica* and *Galium aparine*.

8g

Prominent varied shrub layer - dogwood. guelder rose. rowan. buckthorn over a complex mosaic including *Deschampsia cespitosa*, *Teucrium scorodonia*, *Campanula latifolia*, *C. trachelium*. *Melica uniflora*, *Sanicula europaea*, *Viola riviniana*.

GERANIUM ROBERTIANUM SUB-COMMUNITY

Central type of W8 e.g. Canopy mostly ash. some birch. cherry. yew and whitebeam. Hazel. elder. hawthorn. holly understorey. *Mercurialis perennis* abundant with *Urtica dioica*. *Galium aparine*. *Geranium robertianum*. *Brachypodium sylvaticum*. *Hedera helix* and *Phyllitis scolopendrium*. Good bryophyte cover. Ferns common but not *Athyrium filix-femina*. *Dryopteris filix-mas* or *D. dilatata* (these are more indicative of W9).

ALLIUM URSINUM SUB-COMMUNITY

Woody component as in the central type. Soils deeper and moister so tree/shrub growth more vigorous. Prominence of *Allium ursinum* most distinctive. often carpeting the ground. *Mercurialis perennis* more prominent later in the year.

TEUCRIUM SCORODONIA SUB-COMMUNITY

More species rich and greater structural complexity than other types. Sycamore and wych elm less prominent but oak. yew. beech and limes may be present. Rich ground flora may include additional species - *Melica uniflora*. *M. nutans*. *Myosotis sylvatica*, *Convallaria majalis*. and sometimes *Geranium sanguineum*, *Polygonatum* spp., *Carex digitata* and *Epipactis atrorubens*. Bryophyte cover low because of drier conditions.

Fraxinus excelsior – Sorbus aucuparia – Mercurialis perennis woodland

A community of permanently moist brown soils derived from calcareous bedrock and superficial deposits in the sub-montane climate of north-west Britain commonly found by streams and flush lines in the uplands. The climate of the areas where it occurs is cool, wet, windy and cloudy, conditions unsuitable for the more continental species found in south-east mixed deciduous woods (W8, W10). However, winter temperatures are comparatively mild and this, combined with high humidity, helps give the community a markedly oceanic and winter-green character with an abundance of ferns and bryophytes.

Fraxinus excelsior and *Corylus avellana* are the most abundant woody species but the more continental trees and shrubs sometimes present in W8 (*Tilia cordata, Carpinus betulus, Crataegus laevigata*) are usually absent. *Betula pubescens* and *Sorbus aucuparia* are, by contrast, more common, often co-dominating with *Fraxinus excelsior* and *Corylus avellana. Alnus glutinosa* is occasional in areas of local flushing. There is a trend from well-developed *Fraxinus/Ulmus glabra/ Acer pseudoplatanus/Quercus petraea* high forest with a distinct *Corylus avellana/Crataegus monogyna* understorey to scrubby mixtures of *Corylus avellana, Betula pubescens* and *Sorbus aucuparia* with scattered *Fraxinus excelsior* trees in the far north-west. The latter type is also more characteristic of exposed areas with irregular topography.

Plants in the ground flora form complex mosaics; no single species may achieve dominance and the patterns may be further complicated by the effects of local flushing. *Mercurialis perennis* and *Hyacinthoides non-scriptus* are both frequent but often not as abundant as in the south-east. *Circaea lutetiana, Geum urbanum, Geranium robertianum* and *Brachypodium sylvaticum* may all be common. *Primula vulgaris, Poa trivialis* and *Deschampsia cespitosa*, species uncommon in north-west forms of W8, again become common in W9 whereas *Urtica dioica* and *Galium aparine* occur only occasionally. Ferns are much more prominent in W9 than in W8 – *Dryopteris felix-mas, D. dilatata, Athyrium filix-femina* and *Blechnum spicant* are frequent with occasional *D. borreri* and *Polystichum* spp. Other features which help distinguish W8 and W9 are an abundance of *Oxalis acetosella*, a frequently grassy appearance (*Arrhenatherum elatius, Brachypodium sylvaticum, Deschampsia cespitosa* and *Poa trivialis*), and often a well-developed bryophyte layer. *Eurhynchium praelongum, E. striatum, Plagiomnium undulatum, Thuidium tamariscinum, Mnium hornum* and *Atrichum undulatum* tend to be common with occasional *Cirriphyllum piliferum, Rhytidiadelphus triquetrus, Hypnum cupressiforme, Plagiochila asplenioides* and *Lophocolea bidentata*.

Where soils are calcareous, species like *Homalothecium sericium* and *Neckera crispa* may occur and in wetter areas *Hylocomium splendens* and *Isothecium myosuroides* become more common.

W9

High forest or coppice with a well-defined shrub layer. Fairly short field layer with ferns with other species locally abundant.

— 9a

Less diverse open, scrubby tree layer over a patchy hazel shrub layer. Luxuriant field layer consisting largely of tall herbs.

— 9b

TYPICAL SUB-COMMUNITY

Ash and hazel most abundant with *Betula pubescens* and rowan less frequent. Elm. sycamore and *Quercus petraea* also often present. Hawthorn frequent in the shrub layer. The field layer often has many ferns – *Athyrium filix-femina* and *Dryopteris* spp – with other plants locally abundant between the ferns – *Mercurialis perennis, Hyacinthoides non-scriptus, Brachypodium sylvaticum, Oxalis acetosella, Primula vulgaris, Viola riviniana, Lysimachia nemorum, Geranium robertianum, Poa trivialis* and *Epilobium montanum*. However. *Geum urbanum. Circaea* spp, *Potentilla sterilis. Urtica dioica* and *Galium aparine* are preferential to this sub-community. *Laniastrum galeobdolon* and *Arum maculatum* are more common in the south. *Phyllitis scolopendrium* and other calcicolous ferns are present in limestone crevices. Grasses are only occasional. in spite of grazing. Bryophytes often very abundant.

CREPIS PALUDOSA SUB-COMMUNITY

Open ash. birch. rowan canopy over a patchy hazel understorey, few other woody species present. *Mercurialis perennis. Dryopteris dilatata* and small ground cover plants are less common than in a. However, other plants form a luxuriant field layer including *Filipendula ulmaria. Conopodium majus, Geum rivale* (replacing *G. urbanum* here). *Rumex acetosa, Succisa pratensis, Senecio jacobaea. Stachys sylvatica, Cruciata laevipes. Alchemilla glabra, Vicia sepium, Crepis paludosa. Cirsium helenoides* and *Trollius europaeus.* Grasses are patchily abundant – *Deschampsia cespitosa. Arrhenatherum elatius. Agrostis capillaris. Anthoxanthum odoratum. Holcus* spp. *Dactylis glomeratum* and *Poa trivialis. Ranunculus ficaria* and *Allium ursinum* occur in moister areas. Bryophytes are again abundant, the larger pleurocarps being distinctive.

Quercus robur – Pteridium aquilinum – Rubus fruticosus woodland

A community of base-poor brown earths mainly in the lowlands of southern Britain. The soils on which it occurs show a variety of textures, water and humus regimes, but the pH is usually between 4 and 5.5. Its composition shows a slight continental/continental-southern element, which differentiates it from north western community types, but it is more oceanic than similar European types.

Oak is the commonest tree, usually *Quercus robur* but also *Q. petraea* in places. *Betula pendula* is also abundant, particularly in younger stands. *Acer campestre* tends to be rare and *Fraxinus excelsior* uncommon in the south-east except on acidic but fertile sites. In the north-west *Fraxinus, Acer pseudoplatanus* and sometimes *Ulmus glabra* occur with oak on damper sites usually in the form of high forest or abandoned coppice. *Tilia cordata* and *Carpinus betulus* are locally prominent as in W8. *Castanea sativa* is also locally abundant in this community. Other trees which may be present at low frequencies include *Ilex aquifolium, Sorbus aucuparia, Fagus sylvatica, Prunus avium, Sorbus torminalis* and *Malus sylvestris* with *Alnus glutinosa* and *Populus tremula* on damper soils.

Conifers have been widely planted in W10 but often enough of the ground flora remains to classify the type. *Corylus avellana* is usually abundant in the understorey often with *Crataegus monogyna* and *C. laevigata*.

The ground flora lacks the base-rich indicators such as *Mercurialis perennis* that are common in W8. *Hyacinthoides non-scriptus* and *Anemone nemorosa* are spring dominants, but *Rubus fruticosus, Pteridium aquilinum* and *Lonicera periclymenum* singly or in combination are the commonest species. *Dryopteris felix-mas* and *D. dilatata* may be locally abundant and conspicuous where *Pteridium aquilinum* is sparse. Many stands have a grassy appearance (although this is more pronounced in W11), especially before the emergence of *Pteridium* fronds with *Holcus mollis, Deschampsia cespitosa, Poa trivialis, Milium effusum* or *Melica uniflora*. A wide range of other species occur locally including *Stellaria holostea, Silene dioica, Luzula pilosa, Digitalis purpurea, Solidago virgaurea,* and *Corydalis claviculata*. Bryophyte cover is low with *Eurhynchium praelongum* and *Mnium hornum* as typical species (cf W11, W17).

W10

Anemone nemorosa infrequent although *Castanea sativa* is sometimes a canopy dominant

Anemone nemorosa constant/spring dominant, *Castanea sativa* frequent and often abundant in the canopy.

Hazel frequent, *Holcus lanatus* rare

Hazel rare. *Holcus lanatus* constant but *H. mollis* and *Hyacinthoides non-scriptus* rare.

Ivy rare

Hedera helix constant/abundant in the ground flora.

Ash. sycamore never more than occasional, *Oxalis acetosella* rare.

Ash. sycamore frequent/locally prominent. *Oxalis acetosella* and *Dryopteris dilatata* frequent.

10a
TYPICAL SUB-COMMUNITY

Central type in W10. Dry oak/birch woods. oak sometimes excluded by management, as in coppices of hazel. lime, hornbeam and chestnut. mainly in the south. The commonest shrub is hazel. with some hawthorn. holly. rowan, guelder rose. apple or elder. *Hyacinthoides non-scriptus* dominates in spring with *Rubus fruticosus*. *Pteridium aquilinum* or *Lonicera periclymenum* abundant later. Other species patchy.

10e
ACER PSEUDOPLATANUS - OXALIS ACETOSELLA SUB-COMMUNITY

The most oceanic of the sub-communities and hence more common in the north-west. Oaks present with ash. sycamore and some wych elm. *Betula pendula* quite sparse. Hornbeam and lime absent or rare. Usually high forest structure. Hazel is the most common shrub. *Holcus mollis*, *Dryopteris dilatata* and *Athyrium filix-femina* more common. *Oxalis acetosella*, *Viola riviniana* and a good bryophyte cover are the most distinctive features. Grades into W16 on free-drained acidic soils.

10c
HEDERA HELIX SUB-COMMUNITY

A community of the more Atlantic west side of Britain. Oak is the most common tree, with some beech and ash. Birch rare, over a sparse understorey of hazel, hawthorn, or elder. Holly more abundant than in other sub-communities. *Pteridium aquilinum* frequent but cover low. *Rubus fruticosus/Lonicera periclymenum* abundant. *Hyacinthoides non-scriptus* uncommon. *Hedera helix* carpet is the most distinctive feature. Occasional patches of *Dryopteris felix-mas*, *D. dilatata*, *Galium odoratum*, *Milium effusum*, *Melica uniflora* and *Brachypodium sylvatica*. Possibly transitional to W14.

10d
HOLCUS LANATUS SUB-COMMUNITY

A very tedious community, typical of oak and conifer plantations and of recent secondary birch/oak woods. Understorey sparse or absent. Hazel typically infrequent, but scattered hawthorn. elder, blackthorn. *Pteridium aquilinum* abundant, *Rubus fruticosus/Lonicera periclymenum* common, few other species. *Hyacinthoides non-scriptus* very rare, *Anemone nemorosa* absent. other normal associates of W10 uncommon. Scattered *Holcus lanatus* is the most distinctive feature. usually with tall herb/ruderal/ephemeral species

10b
ANEMONE NEMOROSA SUB-COMMUNITY

Found on winter or spring waterlogged soils on the heavier clays, present on waterlogged plateaus and hollows in undulating topography. *Quercus robur* is the characteristic oak with some birch. ash. sycamore and aspen over a thin hazel understorey. Lime and hornbeam are sparse associates but can be locally abundant. Chestnut often abundant. Cover of *Pteridium aquilinum* is lower than in the rest of W10. Soils are generally too moist for an abundance of *Hyacinthoides non-scriptus* but *Anemone nemorose* carpets in spring are distinctive features.

Quercus petraea – Betula pubescens – Oxalis acetosella woodland

A community of moist, free-draining (but not excessively leached) base-poor brown earth soils in the cooler, wetter north-west of Britain. It is characteristic of substrates that are neither markedly calcareous nor strongly acidic. The character of the community is heavily influenced by grazing.

Quercus petraea is usually dominant (*Quercus robur* and hybrids may occur) with *Betula pubescens* more frequent at higher altitudes and in the extreme north-west. *Betula pendula* also occurs particularly in eastern localities. Hybrids between the birches are present throughout the community. Where *Quercus petraea* dominates it may form a high-forest canopy of tall, well-grown trees or be derived from coppice with a low cover of multi-stemmed crookedly growing individuals. Where birch dominates, the canopy is usually more open, often consisting of widely spaced rather moribund trees. Other trees are scarce. *Fraxinus excelsior* is no more than occasional in some southern stands; *Acer pseudoplatanus* and *Fagus sylvatica* are sparse while *Tilia cordata* is limited to southern examples. *Sorbus aucuparia* and *Corylus avellana* may be locally common, but the understorey is generally less well developed than in W10. The combined cover of all woody species is often low, smaller trees and shrubs being scarce and regeneration limited due to excessive grazing.

Grasses make a major contribution to the ground flora, particularly *Holcus mollis*, *Deschampsia flexuosa*, *Anthoxanthum odoratum*, *Agrostis capillaris* and *A. canina*, although the grasses may be reduced where *Pteridium aquilinum* is vigorous. *Hyacinthoides non-scriptus* is a vernal dominant in western stands but *Anemone nemorosa* becomes more frequent on moister soils and in the more continental regions of north-east Scotland. *Oxalis acetosella* and *Viola riviniana* are characteristic of these permanently moist soils and occur with species indicative of surface leached soils – *Galium saxatile* and *Potentilla erecta*. *Calluna vulgaris*, *Vaccinium* spp. and *Erica* spp. tend to be scarce. Other characteristic herbs include *Teucrium scorodonia*, *Stellaria holostea*, *Luzula pilosa*, *Conopodium majus*, *Veronica chamaedrys*, *V. officinalis*, *Hypericum pulchrum* and *Succisa pratensis* but by mid summer many stands become dominated by *Pteridium aquilinum*. *Lonicera periclymenum* and *Rubus fruticosus* may be abundant particularly in ungrazed stands. Ferns may be conspicuous – *Blechnum spicant*, *Thelypteris limbospera* with less frequent *T. phegopteris*, *Gymnocarpium dryopteris*, *Athyrium filix-femina*, *Polypodium vulgare* and *Polystichum* spp. *Luzula sylvatica* can be a prominent feature in ungrazed stands although some such stands are better referred to W10e.

Bryophytes are common, particularly in sheltered areas such as north-facing slopes and in ravines (the more strictly Atlantic species being found here). Characteristic species are *Rhytidiadelphus squarrosus*, *Pseudoscleropodium purum*, *Thuidium tamariscinum*, *Hylocomium splendens*, *Pleurozium schreberi*, *Dicranum majus*, *Polytrichum formosum* and *Rhytidiadelphus triquetrus*. The bryophyte layer is not however as well-developed as in W17.

Oceanic types
Part of a north-western oceanic continuum from W16. *Hyacinthoides non-scripta* abundant.

More continental types.
Typical of eastern Scotland. Wet climate but cold winters. Oceanic species, eg *Hyacinthoides non-scripta* rare. Canopy a mixture of birch with some oak. *Rhytidiadelphus triquetrus* common.

11a
Quercus petraea abundant, often co-dominant with *Betula pubescens*. Hazel frequent in the shrub layer. Underscrub of *Rubus fruticosus*. *Lonicera periclymenum*, *Dryopteris dilatata* and *D. borreri*.

11b
Birches dominant, oak occasional, hazel scarce. Underscrub and *Dryopteris* spp rare. *Potentilla erecta* and *Hylocomium splendens* constant.

11c
Luzula pilosa, *Anemone nemorosa* and *Trientalis europaeus* constant.

11d
Stellaria holostea, *Hypericum pulchrum*, *Luzula multiflora*, *Ajuga reptans*, *Festuca rubra*, *Veronica officinalis*, *Cerastium fontanum*, *Plagiomnium undulatum* and *Lophocolea bidentata* frequent.

DRYOPTERIS DILATATA SUB-COMMUNITY

Least heavily grazed sub-community. Tall herbs common, grasses less sc. Closed canopy high forests. Rowan often forms a sub-canopy, ash may be present. Hawthorn preferential but rare. Ferns can be abundant. *Deschampsia cespitosa* frequent in moist areas. Bryophytes are reduced because of competition from tall herbs.

BLECHNUM SPICANT SUB-COMMUNITY

The most oceanic type. Grasses abundant with frequent small herbs - *Oxalis acetosella*, *Galium saxatile*, *Potentilla erecta*. Ferns are often conspicuous – *Pteridium aquilinum* dominant on deeper soil. *Blechnum spicant* is characteristic, often luxuriant, *Thelypteris limbosperma*, *T. phegopteris*, *Gymnocarpium dryopteris*, *Dryopteris aemula*, *Athyrium filix-femina* occasional and may be lush in ravines. Bryophytes are abundant particularly on rocky, more leached sites which are transitional with W17. The bulk of the cover is then bryophytes - *Rhytidiadelphus loreus*, *Dicranum majus*, *Pleurozium schreberi*, *Polytrichum formosum*, *Thuidium tamariscinum*, *T. delicatulum*, *Isothecium myosuroides*, *Diplophyllum albicans* and *Plagiochila spinulosa*. Often also a good epiphytic flora particularly on hazel bark.

ANEMONE NEMOROSA SUB-COMMUNITY

Anemone nemorosa prominent in spring followed by *Trientalis europaeus*. *Melampyrum pratense*, *Lathyrus montanus* and *Rubus idaeus* also common. Apart from *Pteridium aquilinum* ferns are generally scarce. Bryophytes extensive but not as luxuriant as in a and b. Some *Pleurozium schreberi*, *Dicranum majus* and *Rhytidiadelphus triquetrus*.

STELLARIA HOLOSTEA-HYPERICUM PULCHRUM SUB-COMMUNITY

Woody cover is c but shift towards *Quercus robur*. *Betula pendula* more pronounced. Grass element more mesophytic – *Holcus mollis* more common. *Festuca rubra* and *Holcus lanatus* preferential. Increase in the less acidophilous herb species. Bryophytes show a similar trend: *Rhytidiadelphus squarrosus*, *Pseudoscleropodium purum*, *Thuidium tamariscinum*, *Eurhynchium praelongum* common: more acidophilous species rare.

Fagus sylvatica – Mercurialis perennis woodland

A community of free-draining base-rich calcareous soils (pH between 7 and 8) in the south-east lowlands of Britain, generally limited to the steeper drift-free faces of chalk escarpments. To the north-west late frosts, low summer temperatures and heavier rainfall hinder beech dominance by their effects on mast production and regeneration, although beech woods can form well to the north-west of its natural range.

Fagus sylvatica is abundant throughout the community. *Fraxinus excelsior* and *Acer pseudoplatanus* are often present, particularly as colonizers of gaps. *Quercus robur* may occur but does not persist under deep shade. *Ulmus glabra* may occur in small amounts. *Sorbus aria* and *Taxus baccata* are characteristic of the community. They can be relicts of an early successional stand or persist in areas where *Fagus sylvatica* does not grow too tall. *Taxus baccata* is shade tolerant and so also persists as an understorey. The shrub layer is usually poorly developed but patches of *Corylus avellana*, *Crataegus monogyna*, *Acer campestre*, *Sambucus nigra* or *Ilex aquifolium* may occur with some *Euonymus europaeus*, *Cornus sanguineus*, *Ligustrum vulgare*, *Viburnum lantana* and *V. opulus*.

The ground flora consists of species characteristic of base-rich soils such as *Mercurialis perennis*, *Sanicula europaea*, *Geum urbanum*, *Circaea lutetiana*, *Arum maculatum*, *Brachypodium sylvaticum*, *Galium odoratum*, *Mycelis muralis* and *Melica uniflora*. Plants indicative of moist base-rich conditions such as *Primula vulgaris*, *Poa trivialis*, *Ajuga reptans*, *Lamiastrum galeobdolon*, *Deschampsia cespitosa* and *Anemone nemorosa* are rare. *Hedera helix* can form a complete carpet and *Rubus fruticosus* is occasionally abundant but where the shade is dense the ground flora may be virtually absent.

Differences between sub-communities are caused by a combination of available soil moisture, slope and soil depth. The *Mercurialis* sub-community (a) occurs on deeper moister soils with the *Sanicula* sub-community (b) on steep slopes with shallow, well drained soils. The *Taxus* sub-community (c) is found on still steeper, usually south facing slopes where the soil is extremely thin and well-drained. If this continuum is extended still further then beech may become rare and the wood becomes a yew type (W13).

Yew rare, never co-dominant, hazel and hawthorn frequent. *Hedera helix* abundant.

Yew constant as a canopy associate, whitebeam occasional, box sometimes present. Hazel and hawthorn rare. Sparse ground flora of *Mercurialis perennis* and *Rubus fruticosus*.

12a

Ash constant, sycamore frequent. Ground flora dominated by mixtures of *Mercurialis perennis*/*Hedera helix*/ *Brachypodium sylvaticum* or *Rubus fruticosus*.

12b

Ash and sycamore rare. *Sanicula europaea, Mycelis muralis, Melica uniflora, Poa nemoralis* and/or privet present.

12c

MERCURIALIS PERENNIS SUB-COMMUNITY

On deeper soils which are fairly moisture retentive, usually on gently sloping ground. These conditions allow *Mercurialis perennis* to produce an extensive canopy excluding other species. Ash and sycamore are frequent with oak occasional. The understorey is patchy but better developed than in b and c - hazel, hawthorn, some field maple, elder and holly. Ground flora is lush but species poor. usually just taller herbs - *Circaea lutetiana. Galium odoratum. Brachypodium sylvaticum. Hedera helix* frequent, other species occasional.

SANICULA EUROPAEA SUB-COMMUNITY

On shallow soils with good drainage, usually on fairly steep slopes. The drier soils limit the growth of *Mercurialis perennis* so the ground flora is more diverse. The tree layer is overwhelmingly dominated by beech but is less well-grown than in a. The shrub layer is also less extensive. *Sanicula europaea* is much more abundant. *Mycelis muralis* is strongly preferential with *Melica uniflora, Poa nemoralis* and *Brachypodium sylvaticum* often giving a grassy appearance. A rich variety of orchids is also characteristic. Bryophytes can be abundant in open areas - *Ctenidium molluscum. Homalothecium sericium* and *Encalypta streptocarpa.*

TAXUS BACCATA SUB-COMMUNITY

On steep, usually south facing slopes with thin very well drained soils. Beech is more slow growing than in other sub-communities so other species such as yew and whitebeam can keep pace and become relatively more common. The canopy height is consequently lower but casts a very deep shade. Shrubs are sparse, some elder, hawthorn, privet, *Clematis vitalba* and occasionally box. The ground flora is often absent because of the shade. scattered *Mycelis muralis, Melica uniflora, Arum maculatum, Circaea lutetiana* and *Geum urbanum* with some shade tolerating mosses like *Eurhynchium praelongum* and *Brachythecium rutabulum.*

Taxus baccata woodland

A community of moderate to very steep, usually south-facing, limestone slopes carrying shallow dry rendzinas. It is almost confined to the chalk of southeast England usually occupying sites too dry for ash (W8) or beech (W12) woods. *Taxus baccata* woods are notably species poor. *Taxus baccata* is the main species, often forming a canopy rarely above 10m high. Few other trees occur. *Sorbus aria* may be present and there can be some *Fraxinus excelsior* as emergent trees. *Fagus sylvatica, Acer pseudoplatanus* and *Quercus robur* may also occur as widely scattered individuals. There is seldom a true understorey, just scattered *Sambucus nigra, Ilex aquifolium* or *Crataegus monogyna* with *Buxus sempervirens* a rare associate. Dead woody remains from a preceding scrub often occur. Juniper for example is a locally common precursor of *Taxus* and remains of this are often present. The field layer is very sparse indeed, at most just a patchy cover of *Mercurialis* with very occasional *Urtica dioica, Hedera helix, Brachypodium sylvaticum, Arum maculatum, Rubus fruticosus, Viola riviniana, Glechoma hederacea* and *Fragaria vesca*. The bryophyte cover is also very low.

Fagus sylvatica – Rubus fruticosus woodland

A community confined to brown earth soils of low base status with moderate to slightly impeded drainage in south Britain. The pH is generally low (4-5) but leaching is limited. The community is usually found on superficial deposits (eg clay with flints) over the southern chalk.

Stands tend to be dominated by *Fagus sylvatica* which forms a closed, even-topped cover of very well-grown trees. However, there can be some structural complexity relating to patterns of natural invasion or management, and also in younger stands. Pollards are quite common especially, for example, in the New Forest.

Quercus robur is the most common associate although with *Q. petraea* on lighter soils. Oak is more frequent in transitions with W10. W10 and W14 can form mosaics, oak having a colonising advantage in younger woods while *Fagus sylvatica* takes over in older stands. Other trees are scarce. *Betula* spp., *Fraxinus excelsior* and *Acer pseudoplatanus* are present in gaps but are not as common as in W12. *Prunus avium* is sometimes found and *Sorbus aria* is present, but again not as common as in W12. The understorey may be limited but *Ilex aquifolium* can be quite dense in oceanic areas. *Taxus baccata, Sorbus aucuparia, Crataegus monogyna, Sambucus nigra, Corylus avellana, Ligustrum vulgare* and *Salix caprea* may occur sporadically.

The ground flora can be sparse or absent where the canopy is dense but *Rubus fruticosus* is usually the commonest species and where the shade is less intense forms a continuous cover up to 1m in height. Because of this cover other plants characteristic of W10 (the edaphic equivalent of W14) are poorly represented. *Hyacinthoides non-scriptus* is infrequent, *Pteridium aquilinum* and *Lonicera periclymenum* are frequent but not abundant. *Hedera helix* is infrequent even in oceanic areas. *Oxalis acetosella* is characteristic before *Rubus fruticosus* attains dominance. Other species often occur only as widely scattered individuals, for example *Holcus mollis, Milium effusum, Melica uniflora, Deschampsia cespitosa, Luzula pilosa, Dryopteris felix-mas, D. dilatata* and *Ruscus aculeatus*. *Galium odoratum* can be abundant but other calcicoles are rare. In gaps and around margins *Rubus idaeus, Digitalis purpurea, Euphorbia amygdaloides* and *Arctium minus* may be present, sometimes with *Epipactis helleborine* and, more rarely, *E. purpurata*.

Bryophyte cover is generally poor, but may be more obvious where dense shade has excluded the herbs as for example around the tree bases. Common species include *Mnium hornum, Isopterygium elegans, Atrichum undulatum, Polytrichum formosum* and *Dicranella heteromalla*. Both *Dicranum scoparium* and *Leucobryum glaucum* are rare, these being more characteristic of W15.

No sub-communities.

Whitebeam a frequent canopy associate.
No shrub layer except occasional elder. Herbs
usually absent.

13a

SORBUS ARIA SUB-COMMUNITY

Sorbus aria is a frequent associate. some ash, beech.
oak and sycamore. Box locally important. Field layer
almost always absent leaving just bare soil and litter.

W13

Whitebeam rare, elder frequent. Sparse ground flora
but constant *Mercurialis perennis*.

13b

MERCURIALIS PERENNIS SUB-COMMUNITY

Yew is the sole canopy tree. The canopy is slightly more open
than a. allowing some elder and occasional spindle. dogwood and
privet with scrambling *Clematis vitalba* and *Tamus communis*.
Herbs more numerous – *Mercurialis perennis* is constant with
some *Urtica dioica. Brachypodium sylvaticum, Rubus
fruticosus. Viola* spp.. *Fragaria vesca. Iris foetidissima.*
However. again most of the ground is bare of herbs.

Fagus sylvatica – Deschampsia flexuosa woodland

A community of very base-poor infertile soil (pH < 4) in the southern lowlands of Britain. It usually occurs on soils that are podzolic with mor humus and free to excessive drainage. Sites usually have a high forest structure, coppice is rare, but some stands have been treated as wood-pasture and retain old pollards of beech. *Quercus robur* is the most common associate in the south. *Q. petraea*, although locally frequent in the south, becomes more abundant in the north. Birch may be present in gaps, *Acer pseudoplatanus*, *Sorbus aria* and *Prunus avium* tend to be scarce and *Fraxinus excelsior* absent. The dense shade of the canopy means that the understorey is often poor or absent. *Ilex aquifolium*, occasionally with some *Taxus baccata*, is the main understorey species.

The ground may be bare of herbs leaving expanses of litter and mor humus. The ground flora is generally patchy, the cover varying according to light penetration through the canopy but in addition *Fagus sylvatica*, being shallow rooted, probably also exerts considerable root competition for water. *Pteridium aquilinum* and *Deschampsia flexuosa* are the most frequent vascular plants. *Rubus fruticosus* is often present but weak compared to its abundance in W14. *Agrostis capillaris* and *Luzula pilosa* also help to separate W14 and W15. *Vaccinium myrtillus* and *Luzula sylvatica* may occur but are largely limited to ungrazed areas. Other species found in places include *Melampyrum pratense*, *Oxalis acetosella*, *Ruscus aculeatus*, *Blechnum spicant* and *Dryopteris dilatata*. Other ferns are rare. The bryophyte layer is often distinctive with *Leucobryum glaucum*, *Dicranella heteromalla*, *Mnium hornum*, *Hypnum cupressiforme*, *Polytrichum formosum*, *Dicranum scoparium* and *Isopterygium elegans*. The community is also renowned for its autumn fungi.

Differences between sub-communities are mainly related to the local light climate.

Fagus sylvatica – Deschampsia flexuosa woodland

A community of very base-poor infertile soil (pH < 4) in the southern lowlands of Britain. It usually occurs on soils that are podzolic with mor humus and free to excessive drainage. Sites usually have a high forest structure, coppice is rare, but some stands have been treated as wood-pasture and retain old pollards of beech. *Quercus robur* is the most common associate in the south. *Q. petraea*, although locally frequent in the south, becomes more abundant in the north. Birch may be present in gaps, *Acer pseudoplatanus*, *Sorbus aria* and *Prunus avium* tend to be scarce and *Fraxinus excelsior* absent. The dense shade of the canopy means that the understorey is often poor or absent. *Ilex aquifolium*, occasionally with some *Taxus baccata*, is the main understorey species.

The ground may be bare of herbs leaving expanses of litter and mor humus. The ground flora is generally patchy, the cover varying according to light penetration through the canopy but in addition *Fagus sylvatica*, being shallow rooted, probably also exerts considerable root competition for water. *Pteridium aquilinum* and *Deschampsia flexuosa* are the most frequent vascular plants. *Rubus fruticosus* is often present but weak compared to its abundance in W14. *Agrostis capillaris* and *Luzula pilosa* also help to separate W14 and W15. *Vaccinium myrtillus* and *Luzula sylvatica* may occur but are largely limited to ungrazed areas. Other species found in places include *Melampyrum pratense*, *Oxalis acetosella*, *Ruscus aculeatus*, *Blechnum spicant* and *Dryopteris dilatata*. Other ferns are rare. The bryophyte layer is often distinctive with *Leucobryum glaucum*, *Dicranella heteromalla*, *Mnium hornum*, *Hypnum cupressiforme*, *Polytrichum formosum*, *Dicranum scoparium* and *Isopterygium elegans*. The community is also renowned for its autumn fungi.

Differences between sub-communities are mainly related to the local light climate.

Quercus spp. – Betula spp. – Deschampsia flexuosa woodland

This is confined to very acidic, oligotrophic soils (pH rarely above 4) in the lowlands and upland fringes. Typically the soils are very free-draining, usually sandy textured and podzolic. Long-established stands occur as high forests, oak-coppice or in wood-pasture but many stands are recent developments on heathland.

Both oaks may be present, with *Quercus robur* more prominent in the south and *Q. petraea* in the north. Birch may also be abundant and dominate in recently formed stands, sometimes with self-sown pine. Other species such as *Fagus sylvatica*, *Castanea sativa*, *Sorbus aria* and *Populus tremula* may occur sporadically but *Acer pseudoplatanus*, *Fraxinus excelsior* and *Ulmus glabra* are almost totally absent. *Sorbus aucuparia* and *Ilex aquifolium* are often present, *S. aucuparia* being more frequent in the north, but *Crataegus* spp. and *Corylus* are very rare, the scarcity of *Corylus avellana* helping to separate W16 from W10. *Frangula alnus*, *Sambucus nigra* and *Rhododendron ponticum* may occur, the last sometimes forming dense thickets.

The field layer is generally species poor. *Deschampsia flexuosa* and *Pteridium aquilinum* are the most consistent species either singly or in mixtures. *Lonicera periclymenum* and *Rubus fruticosus* are not as abundant as in W10. *Vaccinium myrtillus*, *Calluna vulgaris* and *Erica cinerea* may be frequent in ungrazed stands, particularly in the north-west. *Agrostis capillaris* and *Anthoxanthum odoratum* may be more common in grazed situations. *Deschampsia cespitosa* and *Molinia caerulea* mark transitions to damper communities e.g. W4, but sedges are rare. *Luzula pilosa* can occur, as can *L. sylvatica* which may be locally abundant on steep slopes (cf W10, W11). Other species which may be locally common include *Convallaria majalis*, *Galium saxatile*, *Potentilla erecta*, *Teucrium scorodonia*, *Corydalis claviculata*, *Digitalis purpurea*, *Solidago virgaurea*, *Rumex acetosella*, *Hedera helix*, *Blechnum spicant* and *Dryopteris dilatata*.

Dry soils and low atmospheric humidity limit the contribution of bryophytes in the east but they are more abundant to the north and west, particularly *Dicranum scoparium*, *Hypnum cupressiforme*, *Leucobryum glaucum*, *Dicranella heteromalla*, *Isopterygium elegans* and *Pleurozium schreberi*, although both the diversity and abundance are less than in W17.

W16

Oak and/or birch over a species poor ground
flora – only *Deschampsia flexuosa* and
Pteridium aquilinum at all frequent.

16a

Oak *Q. petraea* often dominant with some birch and
rowan. *Vaccinium* more abundant and *Dryopteris
dilatata* frequent, occasional *Dicranella
heteromalla*, *Hypnum cupressiforme*, *Isopterygium
elegans*, *Mnium hornum* and *Lepidozia reptans*.

16b

QUERCUS ROBUR SUB-COMMUNITY

Quercus robur is the typical oak, often the dominant
tree. Birch (locally pine, holly and rowan) more
prominent in secondary woodland on old heathland.

The field and ground layers show few distinctive
features – few bryophytes, some *Calluna vulgaris* and
Erica cinerea in open areas and some *Vaccinium myrtillus*
in areas of high rainfall.

VACCINIUM MYRTILLUS – DRYOPTERIS DILATATA SUB-COMMUNITY

A north-western type marking areas of higher rainfall and humidity,
transitional with sub-montane W17.

Quercus petraea is more usually a canopy dominant, birch limited to gaps
and margins. Some stands are of plantation origin with pine, larch and
beech, some are old coppices. Poorly developed understorey but rowan
is more common in this sub-community. Holly also quite common.

Field layer still *Pteridium aquilinum*, *Deschampsia flexuosa* and ericoids,
but more varied than a. *Vaccinium myrtillus* present on slopes but
Dryopteris dilatata is the best preferential to this community. Increased
bryophyte richness.

Quercus petraea – Betula pubescens – Dicranum majus woodland

A community of very acid often shallow soils in the cooler, wetter north-west of Britain. It occurs on soils where there is a strong tendancy for mor accumulation and where high rainfall leads to strong leaching, so that the soils have a surface pH below 4.

This type is usually dominated by *Quercus petraea* and/or *Betula pubescens* although *Q. robur* is abundant in some localities (eg East Scotland and Dartmoor). The canopy is often low and rather open and in extreme cases the oak may form a very dwarfed canopy. *Betula pubescens* is particularly frequent to the north-west where oak is scarce. The commonest other woody species is *Sorbus aucuparia* often present only as scattered individuals but it can be locally abundant and in the north-west often becomes codominant with *Betula pubescens*. Other tree species are scarce. *Ilex aquifolium* is often restricted by grazing. *Fraxinus excelsior* and *Acer pseudoplatanus* are largely confined to enriched areas (tending to W9). Scattered *Fagus sylvatica* and conifers, originating from planted stock, occur in places. The understorey is variable. *Corylus avellana* is more abundant than in W16 but it tends to be confined to deeper pockets of flushed soil. In the north-west it may combine in the canopy with *Betula pubescens* and *Sorbus aucuparia* to form a scrubby cover.

Grasses, *Pteridium aquilinum* and the ericoid shrubs are characteristic of the field layer of this community. *Deschampsia flexuosa* is common with some *Holcus mollis*, *Anthoxanthum odoratum* and *Agrostis capillaris* on deeper soil, particularly in grazed woods although the last three are more common in W11. *A. canina*, *Festuca ovina* and *Molinia caerulea* may occur but *Holcus lanatus* and *Deschampsia cespitosa* are generally scarce. *Pteridium aquilinum* is abundant but confined to the deeper soil and to areas which are not heavily shaded. *Rubus fruticosus* and *Lonicera periclymenum* (often found in W10, W11) are usually rare. *Vaccinium myrtillus* is often abundant, even in shaded situations, but is sensitive to grazing. *Calluna vulgaris* and *Erica cinerea* occur but are sensitive to shade as well as grazing. Small herbs are not abundant but *Galium saxatile*, *Potentilla erecta*, *Melampyrum pratense*, *Teucrium scorodonia*, *Solidago vigaurea*, *Luzula* spp. or *Oxalis acetosella* often occur. *Hyacinthoides non-scriptus* and *Anemone nemorosa*, by contrast, are infrequent. Ferns are generally abundant, particularly *Blechnum spicant* but also *Thelypteris limbosperma* and *Dryopteris dilatata* with less *D. felix-mas*, *D. borreri*, *Athyrium filix-femina*, *Gymnocarpium dryopteris* and *Polypodium vulgare*. *Hymenophyllum wilsonii*, *H. tunbridgense* and *Dryopteris aemula* may occur on ledges.

The fern element attains its greatest abundance in ravines, as do bryophytes. This last group is particularly abundant in this community. Species to look for include *Dicranum majus*, *Rhytidiadelphus loreus*, *Polytrichum formosum*, *Pleurozium schreberi*, *Plagiothecium undulatum*, *Hylocomium splendens*, *Dicranum scoparium* and *Isothecium myosuroides*. Epiphytic bryophytes and lichens can also be prominent, eg *Cladonia* spp. and *Parmelia saxatilis*.

W17

17a

Isothecium myosuroides and *Diplophyllum albicans* constant and combinations of *Hypnum cupressiforme, Lepidozia reptans, Thuidium delicatulum. Leucobryum glaucum, Campylopus flexuosus, Plagiochila spinulosa, Scapania gracilis* and *Bazzania trilobata.*

17b

Grasses and *Galium saxatile* infrequent.

17c

Galium saxatile, Anthoxanthum odoratum. Agrostis capillaris and *Holcus mollis* constant in a grassy field layer. *Vaccinium myrtillus* much reduced.

17d

Quercus petraea and hazel infrequent, canopy often a single layer – mostly *Betula pubescens* and rowan. *Rhytidiadelphus triquetrus* and *Pseudoscleropodium purum* frequent. *Trientalis europaeus* an occasional preferential.

ISOTHECIUM MYOSUROIDES - DIPLOPHYLLUM ALBICANS SUB-COMMUNITY

Bryophyte layer distinctive. Species characteristic of thin unstable humus abundant, extensive mats covering boulders and logs. Epiphytic cover extends far up tree trunks. Notable western oceanic species present. *Hymenophyllum* spp occasional: other ferns, especially *Blechnum spicant* often lush.

TYPICAL SUB-COMMUNITY

Q. petraea commonest canopy species. *Betula pubescens* only occasional. Hazel common. some holly and rowan. Low grazing pressure. Ericoid shrubs. *Pteridium aquilinum* and *Dryopteris dilatata* abundant. small herbs uncommon. Bryophytes abundant but species characteristic of thin humus absent. Atlantic and epiphytic species may still be common.

ANTHOXANTHUM ODORATUM - AGROSTIS CAPILLARIS SUB-COMMUNITY

A well grazed type. Ericoid shrubs are reduced but grasses are more abundant. Holly and rowan are infrequent. *Pteridium* is frequent and small herbs are quite common. *Digitalis purpurea* and *Rumex acetosa* are weakly preferential. *Rubus fruticosus* occasional - conditions here approach W11. Bryophytes are scarcer but the larger species are present - *Rhytidiadelphus loreus. Hylocomium splendens* and *Plagiothecium undulatum.*

RHYTIDIADELPHUS TRIQUETRUS SUB-COMMUNITY

Quercus robur often replaces *Q. petraea.* Ericoid shrubs are common. *Calluna vulgaris* is preferential. *Pteridium aquilinum* can be dense and small herbs are often common – *Oxalis acetosella, Melampyrum pratense, Potentilla erecta. Viola riviniana* and *Galium saxatile.* Bryophytes are common, the normal community species forming the bulk of the cover but Atlantic species are rare.

HIGH RAINFALL & HUMIDITY ATLANTIC CONDITIONS

LOWER RAINFALL & HUMIDITY CONDITIONS LESS ATLANTIC

Pinus sylvestris – Hylocomium splendens woodland

A community of strongly leached, lime-free, podzolic soils in the cooler parts of Britain – ie the central and north-west highlands of Scotland. Variation in composition is related to the density and age of the pine canopy but climate, soils and the incidence of browsing, grazing and burning are also important in defining sub-communities.

Pinus sylvestris is always the most abundant tree. The canopy is often open, particularly in the west (an arbitrary lower limit of 25% cover separates W18 from ericoid heath) with denser stands in eastern Scotland. Pine tends to occur as a mosaic of well-segregated age-classes and the structual variation is often reflected in the ground flora. The canopy is usually low (13-15m, rarely 20m). Birch is the next most common tree – *Betula pubescens* in the west, *B. pendula* in the east – and *Sorbus aucuparia* may be locally common. Where these three are all abundant they represent a transition to W17 or W11. Mosaics with these types are common. Juniper is also sometimes present as scattered bushes, but can form patches excluding pine, so forming W18/W19 mosaics.

Deschampsia flexuosa is usually present, becoming abundant in grazed situations or under dense shade where ericoid shrubs are reduced. *Vaccinium myrtillus*, *V. vitis-idaea* and *Calluna vulgaris* are more frequent here than in other woodland types, but their abundance is variable. *Calluna vulgaris* is sensitive to shade so is more prominent under open canopies.

Grazing causes a marked reduction in *V. myrtillus* and *Calluna vulgaris* so altering the balance in favour of *V. vitis-idaea*. Other sub-shrubs can be prominent but are less consistent – *Empetrum nigrum*, *Erica tetralix* and *E. cinerea*. Sometimes bryophytes may be the most prominent component of the ground flora, particularly *Hylocomium splendens*, *Dicranum scoparium*, *Pleurozium schreberi*, *Plagiothecium undulatum* and *Rhytidiadelphus loreus*. These are common in other types of acidic woods in the north-west but *Ptilium crista-castrensis* is more restricted and preferential to W18. Also common are *Hypnum jutlandicum*, *H. cupressiforme*, *Polytrichum commune*, *P. formosum*, *P. juniperinum*, *Campylopus flexuosus* and *Aulocomnium palustre*. Lichens, particularly *Cladonia* spp, are often scattered within the bryophyte mat. *Pteridium aquilinum* is usually present but less common than in other acidic woods, despite the generally open canopy. *Molinia caerulea* occurs especially in western stands and in transitions to mires. *Agrostis capillaris*, *A. canina*, *Anthoxanthum odoratum* and *Festuca ovina* can be prominent where grazing is heavy. Other herbaceous species are scarce but may include *Melampyrum pratense*, *Potentilla erecta*, *Trientalis europaea*, *Luzula pilosa*, *Oxalis acetosella* and *Galium saxatile*. Herbs with a strong continental northern distribution are a characteristic of these woods – *Goodyera repens* is most abundant of these with less frequently *Listera cordata*, *Pyrola minor*, *P. media*, *P. rotundifolia*, *Moneses uniflora*, *Orthilia secunda* and *Linnaea borealis*.

W18

Rhytidiadelphus triquetrus constant and Pseudoscleropodium purum frequent in the ground flora.

R. triquetrus and P. purum rare but Acutifolia Sphagna and Dicranum majus frequent. Characteristic of more oceanic areas, higher rainfall, moister, more podzolised soil, thicker peat.

18a Goodyera repens and Erica cinerea constant. Other ericoids sparse. Rhytidiadelphus loreus, Ptilium crista-castrensis Plagiothecium undulatum sparse.

18b Goodyera repens, Erica cinerea rare, ericoids more abundant.

18c

Scattered small herbs but Luzula pilosa, Galium saxatile and Oxalis acetosella rare-absent.

Luzula pilosa, Galium saxatile and Oxalis acetosella frequent.

18d Erica tetralix frequent. Molinia caerulea may also be prominent.

18e Scapania gracilis, Thuidium tamariscinum and Diplophyllum albicans frequent.

ERICA CINEREA-GOODYERA REPENS SUB-COMMUNITY

Sparse field layer, bryophytes prominent. Deschampsia flexuosa is the most common vascular plant.

VACCINIUM MYRTILLUS-V. VITIS-IDAEA SUB-COMMUNITY

Small herbs present but only scattered – Melampyrum pratense, Potentilla erecta. Goodyera repens may be occasional. Bryophytes rich, but may be obscured by ericoids.

LUZULA PILOSA SUB-COMMUNITY

Soils slightly less podzolised and richer than elsewhere. Small herbs frequent. Occasional Anthoxanthum odoratum, Agrostis capillaris, A. canina and Festuca ovina. Some Blechnum spicant.

SPHAGNUM CAPILLIFOLIUM-ERICA TETRALIX SUB-COMMUNITY

Topography uneven, bryophyte covered tussocks on pine stumps and boulders. Calluna vulgaris dominant, other sub-shrubs common. Scattered Erica tetralix characteristic. Some Pteridium aquilinum, Blechnum spicant. Melampyrum pratense and Listera cordata.

SCAPANIA GRACILIS SUB-COMMUNITY

Very similar to d but bryophyte layer richer, more oceanic. Erica tetralix and Molinia caerulea usually absent.

DENSE PINE CANOPY ←——————————————————→ OPEN PINE CANOPY. ASSOCIATED WITH MORE LEACHING IN THE SOIL